MILK

FOR NEW CHRISTIANS

Frank Hamrick & Jerry Dean

PositiveAction
BIBLE CURRICULUM

MILK: FOR NEW CHRISTIANS

written by Frank Hamrick and Jerry Dean

positiveaction.org

Fifth edition 2013
Third printing 2019

Printed in the United States of America

ISBN 978-1-59557-169-4

Edited by C.J. Harris and Jim Lord
Designed by Shannon Brown

Published by

PositiveAction
BIBLE CURRICULUM

TABLE OF CONTENTS

As newborn babes, desire the sincere milk
of the word, that ye may grow thereby.

—1 Peter 2:2

As a new Christian, you might be wondering what to make of your young faith. What does God expect of you? What are you supposed to know? More importantly, who are you supposed to be?

It might seem a little overwhelming, but God doesn't expect you to figure out everything at once. He's already changed you into someone new (2 Cor. 5:17), and He promises to continue His work in you (Phil. 1:6). So don't trust your ability to learn or do or be. Trust God, and let Him teach you, guide you, and mold you.

That's not to say you don't have some work ahead of you. This book offers you milk from God's Word—that is, passages from Scripture which teach you basic doctrines about your faith and about God. You might not have studied the Bible before, so even these simple truths could be difficult to learn.

So ask God to open your heart. Ask Him to help you understand His Word, so that you can grow stronger and wiser—and closer to your Savior.

1

HOW DID I BECOME A CHRISTIAN?

The Bible talks a lot about salvation, but what does this word really mean?

Normally, we might imagine a person getting "saved" from a burning house or a rushing river. But when the Bible uses the word *salvation*, it's talking about something far more important than rescue from physical injury or death.

Biblical salvation refers to two things—first, our rescue from hell and eternal separation from God, and second, our restoration and adoption as God's children, in this world now and in heaven forever.

Some Christians, therefore, call themselves "saved" to recognize that God has rescued them *from* their sin and *to* His family.

But how does this salvation happen?

GOOD WORKS DON'T SAVE

Maybe you're asking, "Don't I have to do something to get saved? Aren't good or noble actions necessary to get me into heaven?"

Let's see what God says through His Word, the Bible. Turn to Romans 3:9–12.

- Verse 9 teaches that Jews and Gentiles (non-Jews) are the same in that they are both under _____.

- What do you think this means? _____
  _____
  _____
  _____

- Verse 10 describes what we really are in God's sight. How many are righteous—that is, right with God?
  _____

- According to verse 11, how many people really seek God? _____

- According to verse 12, how many people, from God's perspective, do good? _____

It's a fair question. But what does the Bible mean by "good"?

- As far as making other people happy, any of us can do good. We can share, give, and even die helping others—all as sinners unredeemed by Christ.

- But so far as pleasing God, no person can do good on his own. Romans 8:8 says that those who are in the flesh—that is, those who haven't trusted Christ for their salvation—_____ please God.

Without Christ, we cannot please God at all, and we certainly couldn't please God enough for Him to overlook our sin.

GOD IS HOLY

Read Leviticus 11:44 and answer the following questions.

- What did God require of Israel? _____
  _____

- Why must they be holy? _____
  _____

Read Habakkuk 1:13. Here the prophet is talking to God, and we learn that God is so pure, so holy, that He cannot even

_____.

God is perfectly holy, and He demands holiness from every individual.

- Romans 3:23 tells us that _____ have sinned.

- Can people that have sinned—that are imperfect—please a perfectly holy God by their own works? ☐ Yes ☐ No.

As we shall see, God is so holy that even our good works appear to Him as sinful.

Because God is holy, our sins separate us from Him.

- What does Romans 6:23 tell us is the wage, or reward, for our sin? _____

SALVATION IS A GIFT

- According to Romans 6:23, how does a person gain eternal life? _____
  _____

- What do you have to do to get a gift? _____
  _____

- If a person offers you a gift, do you tell them, "Well, that's great, but let me pay for it and earn it"?
  ☐ Yes ☐ No

- Is there any way you can work for a free gift?
  ☐ Yes ☐ No

If you work for a gift, it is no longer a gift—it's a wage. Read Romans 6:23 again. Death is the wage we deserve for our sin. Eternal life—that is, salvation—is the gift that God offers us through Jesus Christ. What can we do but accept it?

OUR RIGHTEOUS DEEDS ARE WORTHLESS

- How does Isaiah 64:6 describe the so-called righteous things we try to do?_____
  _____
  _____

These filthy rags or garments refer to the kind of bandages someone might place over an open sore. Once removed from the wound, the bandages are disgusting, polluted garbage. This is how God views our works. Our intentions might be good, but our sinful nature corrupts even our best efforts.

WHEN DOES A PERSON BECOME A CHRISTIAN?

The following four things happen as a person becomes a Christian.

He Recognizes That He Is a Condemned Sinner Before a Holy God

Throughout the Bible, we see people confronted with their sin. How did the following admit their sinfulness?

- David—2 Samuel 12:13 _____

  _____

  _____

- Isaiah 6:5 _____

  _____

  _____

He Recognizes What Christ Has Done for Him

In Acts 8:26–40, a royal treasurer from Ethiopia asked one of Christ's disciples, Philip, to explain the meaning of Isaiah 53. Philip showed him how the passage prophesied that a Savior would come and die for our sins.

Salvation would not be possible had Christ not paid for our sins on the cross (1 Pet. 1:17–19; Rom. 5:6). Without an understanding of Christ's saving work on the cross, a person cannot be saved.

God's holiness and justice require death for our sins (Rom. 6:23). But the *gospel*—that is, the good news—is that Christ died in our place.

He Repents of His Sin and Flees to Christ for Salvation

- According to 2 Corinthians 7:10, what does godly sorrow, or grief, produce? _____
- And what does this lead to? _____

To *repent* is to turn around, to change your mind and therefore your direction.

- How does a person gain repentance (2 Tim. 2:25)?

_____

God-given repentance is not just self-pity or guilt for having done wrong. Those attitudes don't turn us to God for salvation.

But how do we know that our repentance is the kind that leads us to salvation? Two signs accompany God-given repentance:

1. As mentioned before, we will have godly _____ for our sin (2 Cor. 7:10). This is an actual hatred of our sin, a deep desire to be cleansed of it.

2. We will desire Christ. We will see Him as our precious cornerstone (1 Pet. 2:7). We will understand how dependent we are on Him.

- Read Matthew 13:44. *To 48* When the man found treasure in the field, how did he respond? What was his attitude?

_____

_____

That treasure represents Christ. When a person truly repents of his sin, he realizes that Christ is more valuable and desirable than all the treasures on Earth. He will do anything to gain that glorious treasure. *and leave behind sin all wickedness in his life!*

He Believes on the Lord Jesus Christ with All His Heart

- Read John 3:16. According to this verse, who will be given eternal life? _____

_____

Salvation is not a business transaction—the kind where God offers to save us if we will believe, and we just say, "Okay, I believe." As with repentance, some so-called belief does not lead to salvation.

- James 2:19 tells us that the _____ also believe that God exists. But this kind of belief will not save them.

The kind of belief Jesus spoke of to Nicodemus (John 3:16) leads to salvation. How is it different from the belief that the demons have?

True belief grows from a knowledge of . . .

- God's holiness
- Our sinfulness
- Our utter helplessness to save ourselves

We can then turn to our precious Savior, Christ, who alone can save us, trusting Him to save us from sin by His work on the cross.

And when we come to Him, He redeems us, changes us, *saves* us.

Complete This Section Without Looking Back at the Lesson

1. Who has sinned? _____

2. What is the reward for our sin? _____

3. Can people naturally do anything pleasing to God?
   ☐ Yes   ☐ No

4. Can people do good deeds in the sight of other people?
   ☐ Yes   ☐ No

5. According to Romans 6:23, can we earn eternal life—that is, salvation? Or is it a gift of God? _____
   _____

6. Before salvation, how do our attempts at good deeds appear to God? _____
   _____
   _____

7. What must a person do to be saved? _____
   _____

8. What four things take place when a person is truly saved?
   _____
   _____
   _____
   _____
   _____
   _____
   _____

In Psalm 119, the psalmist writes of a love for God's Word, which leads to a desire to hide, or keep, that Word in your heart (vs. 11). The best way to keep the Word in your heart and mind is to read and memorize it.

Learn the following verses. They will remind you that salvation is a free gift, one available to all who believe on Christ and depend on Him alone to save them.

Verses to Memorize

- Ephesians 2:8, 9

2

THE ASSURANCE OF SALVATION

Can a person know for sure whether he has received salvation? Some people teach that we can only hope to be saved, that we won't know we're going to heaven until we get there.

But Scripture teaches us that we can have certainty *now*—not because of what we do, but because of Christ. In fact, God included a book in the Bible just to assure believers that they have eternal life in Him (1 John).

God uses the following ways to help Christians know they are truly His children.

CHRIST'S LIFE ASSURES

When God saves a person, something happens to him on the inside.

The Old Sinner Dies

- Read Galatians 2:20. In the first phrase of this verse, what did Paul say happened to him? _____
  _____

Paul's former identity as a sinner is gone. Because of Christ's sacrifice, sin no longer defines or bounds us.

God Places a New Life Within Us

- According to Galatians 2:20, a new life arises within the believer. Where did this life come from? _____
  _____

- But someone must sustain this life. Look at Galatians 2:20 again. On what person do we place our faith?
  _____

- And what does this verse say He has done for us?
  _____
  _____
  _____

- To summarize: in Colossians 3:4, what does Paul call Christ? _____

Christ died once to pay for our sins (Rom. 5:6), but He rose again three days later.

- According to Romans 6:9, what did Christ prove by His resurrection? _____

    _____

    _____

- Can He ever die again? _____

Psalm 110 is a song about Christ, written 1000 years before He was born on Earth. It describes His power and authority, using several different pictures as examples.

One picture, or type, of Christ is Melchizedek, an ancient King-Priest who lived during Abraham's day, in a city that would later become Jerusalem. Hebrews 7 argues that Jesus became a priest for us in the same order, or tradition, as Melchizedek.

- Psalm 110:4 prophesies that Christ will be a priest like Melchizedek. How long will He keep this position?

    _____

- According to Revelation 11:15, how long will Christ reign, or rule? _____

Jesus Christ, our very life, our eternal priest and connection to God, will forever keep us safe in Him.

> *But couldn't Christ leave me?*

Christ Will Never Leave Us

- Read Hebrews 13:5. What will Christ never do?

    _____

We Who Have Christ Have Eternal Life

Read 1 John 5:11–13 and answer the following questions.

- Who gives eternal life? _____
- Does everyone possess eternal life? ☐ Yes   ☐ No

- Who has eternal life? Where does it come from? _____

  _____

  _____

- Who does not have eternal life? _____

  _____

- To whom did John write these verses? _____

  _____

  _____

- According to these verses, can you *know* that you have eternal life? ☐ Yes   ☐ No

Since Christ—who will never die—lives in believers, and since He has promised to never leave us, then we can never go to hell. Christ's life assures us of eternal salvation.

GOD'S WORD ASSURES

Read Acts 16:30, 31; Romans 10:9, 13; John 3:16. Now answer the following questions.

- In your own words, what must a person do to be saved?

  _____

  _____

  _____

- Can God lie (Titus 1:2)? ☐ Yes   ☐ No
- Did God say He would save you if you put your faith and trust in Him? ☐ Yes   ☐ No
- Do you trust Him for salvation? ☐ Yes   ☐ No
- Then according to God's Word, are you saved?
  ☐ Yes   ☐ No

GOD'S HANDS ASSURE

Read John 10:27–29. These verses show that we, as believers, are in Christ's hand (vs. 28) and in God the Father's hand (vs. 29).

- Can anyone take us out of God's hands? ☐ Yes   ☐ No

- Study verse 28. *Perish* in this verse means to suffer in hell. If a person is God's child, safe in His hands, will he ever perish? ☐ Yes ☐ No

- After reading these verses, do you think it is up to you to keep yourself saved? ☐ Yes ☐ No

- Look at 1 Peter 1:5. According to this verse, what protects or keeps us through faith to our salvation?

_____

_____

God is all-mighty (Gen. 17:1). He can do whatever He decides to do. His power knows no limits, just as our trust in Him should know no limits.

DEALING WITH DOUBTS

Sometimes you may wonder whether you are saved. Our flesh, vulnerable to spiritual weakness and attack, can doubt God's goodness and power. This is common, especially for new believers, or for believers who have just begun to think critically about their faith.

> *But I just don't feel saved.*

Read John 1:12.

- What does God give to those who receive Jesus Christ?

_____

_____

- According to this verse, what have you become by receiving Christ? _____

- Do you have to *feel* like you are the child of your parents to actually be their child? ☐ Yes ☐ No

- Some mornings you may get out of bed and not even feel alive. Does that mean you are not living? ☐ Yes ☐ No

- You are now a child of God—is that a fact or a feeling?
  _____

Complete This Section Without Looking Back at the Lesson

1. How does Christ's life give us assurance that we are eternally saved? _____
   _____

   _____

   _____

2. Who possesses eternal life? _____
   _____

3. Do you possess eternal life? ☐ Yes ☐ No

4. How do you know? _____
   _____

   _____

5. What verse of Scripture teaches that you can know you have eternal life? _____

6. In your own words, what does a person do to be saved?
   _____

   _____

   _____

7. What verses teach that you're in God's hands?
   _____

8. According to 1 Peter 1:5, what protects, or keeps, us?
   _____

   _____

9. List three things that assure us of our salvation.
   _____

   _____

   _____

Verses to Memorize

- 1 John 5:13
- Romans 10:9

3

THE IMPORTANCE
OF GOD'S WORD

Now that you know you're saved—that you have become a new creature (2 Cor. 5:17)—you may ask, "What do I do now? There's got to be more to it than this!" You're right—there is more, *lots* more.

But you're not alone. A loving parent would not leave a newborn infant to take care of himself, and neither does God leave a newborn Christian to grow for himself. But how do you grow as a Christian?

The Word of God is the means by which we grow and become stronger Christians (1 Pet. 2:2). It makes sense that the more we read about someone, the more we will know about that person. God is the author of the Bible. As we read His Word, we will learn more about Him and about how we should live for His glory.

WHAT GOD SAYS ABOUT HIS WORD

- According to Psalm 138:2, how has God shown the importance of what He says? _____

  _____

  _____

- According to Matthew 5:17–18, why did Christ come to Earth? _____

- In the same passage, how much of God's Word did Christ say was true—that is, how much will be fulfilled or accomplished? _____
  Note also John 10:35.

- In John 5:39, what did Christ say was one purpose of the Old Testament Scriptures? _____

  _____

- In Matthew 24:35, what did Christ say would not happen to His words?_____

  _____

- According to 2 Timothy 3:16, what is true about all Scripture? _____

  _____

- According to James 1:21, how does God use His Word if we receive it? _____

Answer the following questions from 1 Peter 1:23.

- How is a person born again? _____

  _____

- How does this verse describe the Word of God?

  _____

- What do you believe the verse means when it calls the Word an incorruptible, or imperishable, seed?

  _____

  _____

Note what the following verses say about the purpose of the Bible.

- According to Romans 10:17, how does a person find the faith to trust Christ? _____

  _____

- Why was the Gospel of John written (John 20:30–31)?

  _____

  _____

SEVEN BLESSINGS OF STUDYING THE WORD OF GOD

Look up the following verses about studying God's Word. Match them with the blessings they provide. Write the correct letters in the blanks. Studying the Bible will help us . . .

	1. Keep from sin	A. Psalm 119:11
	2. Build up, or grow, spiritually	B. Psalm 119:99
	3. Live and have hope	C. Psalm 119:105
	4. Know the truth	D. Psalm 119:116
	5. Know where I'm going	E. Psalm 119:160
	6. Understand, or have insight	F. Acts 20:32
	7. Know good from evil	G. Hebrews 5:14

YOU SHOULD DO SEVEN THINGS WITH GOD'S WORD

Look up the passages below, and write what you should do with God's Word.

- Revelation 1:3 _____

  _____

- Acts 24:14 _____

  _____

- Revelation 22:7; James 1:22 _____

  _____

  _____

- 2 Timothy 2:15 _____

  _____

- Psalm 119:11 _____

  _____

  - What is the best way to hide, or keep, it? _____

    _____

    _____

- 1 Timothy 4:15 _____

  _____

  - To *meditate* is to spend time and effort thinking and focusing on God's truth.

- Philippians 2:16 _____

  _____

1. What is the only way a person can grow in the Lord?
    _____

2. Name seven things a study of the Word of God will do
    in your life. _____
    _____
    _____
    _____
    _____
    _____
    _____
    _____
    _____
    _____
    _____
    _____

3. How much of God's Word did Christ say was true?
    _____

4. How does a person find the faith to trust Christ?
    _____
    _____

5. List three ways you should treat the Word of God.
    Include a Scripture reference with each. _____
    _____
    _____
    _____
    _____
    _____

Verses to Memorize

- 2 Timothy 2:15
- 2 Timothy 3:16
- Psalm 119:9, 11

4

HOW TO STUDY
THE WORD

Would you look in a dictionary to find a phone number? Of course not. To use a book effectively, you must first know its purpose.

The same is true of the Bible. God gave us His Word for a purpose—to reveal Himself to us. The key to reading the Bible is to look for God in every passage and every verse you see.

The Word of God will also teach you about yourself. In James 1:22–25, the writer presents the Word of God as a mirror that shows us our innermost heart. As we look into this mirror, God changes us to become more like His Son, Christ.

LOOK FOR GOD IN THE PASSAGE

God's Word was written primarily to reveal God—who He is and what He does. If we read the Bible and don't see Him, we miss the whole point of Scripture.

- How did the scribes and Pharisees illustrate this idea in John 5:37–40? _____

  _____

- When you read the Word, take a sheet of paper and divide it into three sections, as in the table below.

What God Does	Who God Is
How God Works	

Under "What God Does," record everything you see God doing in the passage—even small things, like when Jesus walked, talked, and healed people. Under "Who God Is," record any attributes and characteristics this passage reveals about God (holiness, mercy, grace, justice, and others). Under "How God Works," record what you learn about the way God works (His plans, His concerns about our happiness, His interest in our spiritual welfare, and more).

Make a copy of the preceding table on a separate sheet of paper, and fill it in using Mark 2:1–12.

UNDERSTAND THE "STORY" OF THE BIBLE

The Bible is not a collection of stories that teach good moral truth. Rather, it is one story with one ultimate goal. Simply put, *the Bible is the story of God's glory*. The Bible begins with God (Gen. 1:1) and concludes with His grace (Rev. 22:21).

> *The purpose of God's Word is to tell us the*
> *story of God's glory and grace.*

The Bible is God's self-revelation. It's His autobiography. As such, we should read it to learn His story and His glory. So what is this story of His glory?

The Story of God's Glory

- God made mankind to glorify Him (Isa. 43:7; Gen. 1–2).

- Satan wanted to steal God's glory, so he deceived Adam and Eve, thereby blinding all mankind to God's glory (Gen. 3; 1 Cor. 4:4, 6).

- God, knowing this would happen, set in motion an eternal plan to restore mankind's state so that we could once more see God's glory and enjoy Him. We call this God's Plan of Redemption.

The Plan of Redemption

God's plan of redemption is a sub-plot of the story of God's glory.

- God made a nation, Israel, from Abraham's descendants (Genesis).

- God prepared a land, Canaan, where that nation would live, and He brought those people to that land (Exodus – Joshua).

- God chose from Abraham's descendants the line of David, through which a Redeemer would come (1 Samuel).

- God protected and preserved that line through famine, war, and mass exile (1 Samuel – Nehemiah).

- God used the prophets to reveal the coming of a future Messiah—an Anointed One—who would redeem mankind (Old Testament Prophets, Psalms).

- In God's timing, that Messiah, Jesus Christ, was born of a virgin, Mary, who was a direct descendant of David. Jesus died on a cross to pay for mankind's sin, and He arose from the dead to save and redeem us so that we could once more see God's glory (Matthew – John).

- Today, God is saving—that is, redeeming, restoring, regenerating—a people to glorify His name (Acts 15:14) and to praise Him to the whole world (1 Pet. 2:9).

The Conclusion to the Story of God's Glory

All people will one day glorify God, bow to Christ as Lord, and give Him glory (Phil. 2:11). Thus, God will fulfill the purpose He intended for mankind from the beginning.

We must understand this story when we read the Bible. The Bible is not about David, or Moses, or Ruth—it's about a God that uses imperfect men and women to reflect His glory. It's not about ancient heroes we should imitate—it's about God's great plan for His glory and our redemption.

Every story we read, every chapter and book we study, every command or encouragement we see in the Bible—they all fit inside that story. When we fail to see a passage in the light of God's glory, we will miss the point of Scripture.

As a second exercise, take a sheet of paper and divide it into 4 equal sections labeled as follows.

God's Actions—what God does in this passage
His Glory—what you learned about the character and attributes of God in this passage
His Grace—what you learned about God's grace, Christ's work, the cross, and the gospel in this passage
Other Thoughts—other things you may have learned or realized while reading this passage

Read Genesis 1:1–8 and fill in the above sections as you read and meditate.

LOOKING INTO THE MIRROR OF THE WORD

Read James 1:19–27 and answer the following questions.

- What should you be quick to do according to verse 19?

  _____

- But you shouldn't stop there. According to verse 22, what's our responsibility after hearing the Word?

  _____

  _____

- What will happen if you do both of these things (vs. 25)?

  _____

  _____

  _____

- According to 2 Corinthians 3:18, what are the results of seeing God's glory in the Bible? _____

  _____

  _____

  _____

As we read God's Word, the Holy Spirit convicts us of ways we fall short of God's glory. He then uses the Word to correct us and make us more like Christ.

In short, as we seek God in His Word, He changes us to be more like Him.

DEPENDENCE ON THE HOLY SPIRIT

Read 1 Corinthians 2:12–14 and answer the following questions.

- Who cannot understand God's Word? _____
  _____

- Who can understand God's Word? _____
  _____

- What is the only way a person can understand the Word? _____
  _____
  _____

Complete This Section Without Looking Back at the Lesson

1. What is the Bible about? _____
   _____

2. What was God's purpose for creating mankind?
   _____
   _____

3. What is God doing today as part of the Plan of Redemption? _____
   _____
   _____

4. What are the results of seeing God's glory in the Bible?
   _____
   _____
   _____

5. What is the only way a person can understand God's Word? _____
   _____

6. Why can't unsaved people understand the Word?

_____

_____

_____

- 1 Corinthians 2:14
- Psalm 119:97

5
PRAYER

We have learned that the Bible is God's Word. When we study it, the Lord speaks to us. But fellowship with our Heavenly Father goes both ways—we must also talk to Him each day.

If you never spoke to your parents or friends, what sort of relationship would you have? A strained one at best. We must listen to God, but He also asks us to spend much time talking to Him. To help you get started, here are some basic things you should know about prayer.

PRAYER AND SIN

- As you'll remember from previous lessons, sin hurts our fellowship with God. Read Psalm 66:18, and state in your own words what this verse means. _____

  _____

  _____

  _____

  _____

How do we, as Christians, get rid of sin? Do we have to be saved all over again? No—we've already learned that we have become children of God forever, and nothing and no one can change that.

So what do we do if we sin? Read 1 John 1:9.

- What should we do about sin? _____

  _____

- Then what two things will God do? _____

  _____

  _____

Note Nehemiah's prayer in Nehemiah 1:4–11.

- How did Nehemiah begin the prayer (vs. 5)?

  _____

  _____

- After this praise, what did he do (vs. 6, 7)?_____

  _____

- What did he ask God to do in verses 8–10?

  _____

  _____

- And what did he plead in verse 11? _____

  _____

  _____

We could outline Nehemiah's prayer as follows:
1. Adoration and worship
2. Confession of his sin
3. Claiming God's promises
4. Asking for help

- Most often we are only interested in doing one of the above. Which is it? _____

But God will not answer prayer if we do not confess our sin.

WHY WE CAN PRAY

Study 1 Timothy 2:5 and 1 John 2:1. In these two passages the words *mediator* and *advocate* mean basically the same thing: Christ is literally your Lawyer, pleading your case before God, the Judge.

Christ justifies us by covering us with the sacrifice of His blood. So when God looks at our sin, He sees only the righteousness of Christ. Christ not only paid the debt of our sin, but He also gave us the riches of eternal life, free for the taking. Because of His work, we can stand before God and speak to Him as one of His children.

- Read Hebrews 10:19–22. With what attitude can we approach God in prayer?_____

  _____

- According to verse 19, what makes this attitude possible? _____

  _____

HOW TO PRAY

Read Ephesians 5:20; John 14:6, 13, 14; 15:16; 16:23, 26–27. Based on these verses, answer the following questions.

To Whom to Pray

- How does Jesus begin His prayer in Matthew 6:9?

  _____

  _____

- Should you pray to the Father, the Son, or the Holy Spirit? _____

- According to these verses, would it be best to pray, "Dear Jesus"? ☐ Yes ☐ No

In Whose Name to Pray

- What one phrase occurs over and over again in these verses? _____

- Whose name are these verses speaking of?

  _____

- Therefore, in whose name should we pray?

  _____

In Whose Power to Pray

When Christ went back into heaven, He promised to send Someone to help us. Read John 14:16; 15:26; 16:7

These verses all use the same Greek word, *Parakletos*, which literally means "the One who comes beside to help." It's the same word used in 1 John 2:1 to describe Christ helping us before God, but here the term refers to a different "Helper" or "Comforter."

- Who is this Comforter (John 15:26)? _____

- What does He do for us when we pray (Rom. 8:26)?

  _____

DEFINITION OF PRAYER

Prayer is worship—addressed to the Father, in the name of the Son, in the power of the Holy Spirit.

THE PRAYERS GOD WILL ANSWER

God hears even the simplest, heartfelt prayers, but His Word includes instructions for those who want to see His hand at work. Read the following passages and write down the requirements for true prayer.

- Matthew 21:22 _____

_____

- John 16:23 _____

_____

- James 5:16–17 _____

_____

- 1 Peter 3:12 _____

_____

- 1 John 5:14–15 _____

_____

WHY GOD ANSWERS PRAYER

According to the verses below, why does God answer prayer?

- John 14:13 _____

_____

- John 16:24 _____

_____

REASONS FOR OUR PRAYER

- Matthew 6:9–13 lists six things we should pray for. What are they? _____

_____

_____

_____

_____

_____

WHERE AND WHEN TO PRAY

Answer the following questions:

- When did the prophet Daniel pray (Dan. 6:10)?

  _____

- What about Isaiah (Isa. 26:9)?_____

  _____

- In Mark 1:35, when and where did Christ pray?

  _____

  _____

- In Matthew 6:5–6, where did Christ say we should pray? _____

- Based on the verses above, how can you set aside a time and place to fellowship with God? _____

  _____

  _____

Complete This Section Without Looking Back at the Lesson

1. What one thing hinders prayer? _____

2. What should you always do before you ask God for anything?_____

   _____

3. Why is it possible to pray to God? _____

   _____

   _____

4. To whom should you pray, in whose name, and in whose power should you pray? _____

   _____

   _____

   _____

5. Why does God answer prayer? _____

   _____

   _____

   _____

6. What is prayer? _____

_____

_____

_____

Verses to Memorize

- 1 Timothy 2:8
- Psalm 66:18
- 1 Peter 3:12

6

SHARING OUR FAITH

You may have heard about the importance of witnessing or sharing your faith. After all, God used someone in some way to reach out to you. But what exactly is a witness, and why is it important to be one?

In a court case, a witness tells others about what he has seen or experienced. And in the Christian life, a witness does the same thing. He tells others about the glorious God who redeemed him, and he shows them how they can know this same God.

WHY SHOULD WE WITNESS?

We Want the Whole World to See His Glory

As we experience God's grace and love, we will naturally want others to know about Him.

- How did David express this desire (Ps. 71:24a)?

  _____

  _____

  _____

Read the following verses, and state what drove Paul to be a missionary to the whole world.

- Romans 1:5 _____

  _____

- 2 Corinthians 5:14 _____

  _____

God gave Paul a desire to show everyone how wonderful, awesome, beautiful, and gracious God is. Sharing our faith is merely bragging about the God we love—because He first loved us.

God Wants Us to Witness

- What did Christ say He would make of His followers (Matt. 4:19)? _____

- What title did Christ give us (Acts 1:8)?_____

  _____

- Why did God gather us together as this "holy nation" (1 Pet. 2:9)? _____

_____

God Chose to Use Us to Reflect Himself

- According to James 1:18 and 1 Peter 1:23, what is the tool through which people are born into God's family?

_____

- According to Romans 10:14, what must happen before a person believes on Christ? _____

_____

_____

- How does this verse challenge you? _____

_____

_____

Our Faith Grows as We Share It

One of the best ways to learn something is to teach it. God can use our work and preparation to increase our faith and deepen our love for Christ.

What if people laugh at me?

WHY SOME DON'T SHARE THEIR FAITH

- Why might many Christians not proclaim God to others (Pro. 29:25)? _____

_____

- Why was Paul not ashamed to preach the good news of Christ (Rom. 1:16)?_____

_____

_____

God gave Paul an excitement about His character and work through Christ. This attitude grows from a love for God and other people, and there's no better way to show that love than to share our Savior with others.

OUR LIFE MAKES A DIFFERENCE

What we do is a reflection of who we are, and if we want to share with others how Christ has changed us, we should not do anything that would unnecessarily turn others away from God.

The gospel isn't preached by words alone, but also by action. God uses what we say and what we do to reflect Him, and if we say things that aren't backed up by our lives, people will notice.

- Read Philippians 1:27. What did Paul challenge the Philippian Christians to do? _____
  _____
  _____

- Read 1 Peter 2:11–15. From what is a Christian to abstain? _____
  _____

- People may accuse us of doing evil—falsely or truthfully— but what will silence them (vv. 12–15)? _____
  _____

HOW TO WITNESS

When witnessing to a person who has not accepted Christ, share the following four truths. In this section, wherever you see a verse reference followed by blanks, write out the verse and underline any key phrases you believe might be helpful.

God Is Holy, and We Are All Sinners

This first basic fact is essential to understanding our need. We must see God's standard of holiness and how far short we've fallen from it. The following verses state our sinfulness.

- Romans 3:10, 23 _____
  _____

* Isaiah 53:6 _____

_____

_____

_____

You can also use Galatians 3:22, Jeremiah 17:9, and Ecclesiastes 7:20.

God Will Punish Us for Our Sin

After the first point, an unbeliever may think, "So what? Yes, I'm a sinner, but everyone else is a sinner as well. What's so bad about that?" We must recognize the awful consequences of being a sinner.

Death

* Romans 6:23 _____

_____

_____

* Ezekiel 18:4b _____

_____

Hell and the Lake of Fire

* Luke 16:23 _____

_____

_____

* Revelation 20:15 _____

_____

_____

Christ Suffered Our Punishment for Us

Now for the good news. After you have shown the person that he is a sinner—and therefore under the condemnation of death and hell—you show him God's love and God's provision for his sin.

Christ Was Born to Save Us from Our Sin

- Matthew 1:21 _____
  _____
  _____
  _____
  _____

He Came to Take Away Our Sin

- John 1:29 _____
  _____
  _____
  _____
  _____

He Bore Our Sins

- 1 Peter 2:24 _____
  _____
  _____
  _____
  _____

He Died for Us

- Romans 5:6, 8 _____
  _____
  _____
  _____
  _____

Here you should emphasize substitution to an unbeliever. Christ took our place on the cross. We were condemned to die and suffer in hell, but because of His love for us, He came to Earth and suffered our hell in our place. God poured out His wrath on Christ as payment for our sin.

If Christ paid our debt on the cross, then we have nothing left to pay. If you owe a debt and someone pays it for you, there is nothing else to do but accept it. Christ paid the debt for sin, and He now asks us to do the following:

Confess Him as the Lord of Our Lives

- Romans 10:9 _____

  _____

  _____

  _____

Trust What He Did on the Cross to Provide Payment for Our Sin

- John 3:16 _____

  _____

  _____

  _____

  _____

Help! The person wants to be saved. What do I do now?

URGE HIM TO TRUST CHRIST AS HIS LORD AND SAVIOR

We must be very careful at this point. Salvation does not happen because you trick or manipulate someone into saying the right things. True repentance and regeneration is the work of the Holy Spirit.

- When Paul's jailor asked how to be saved in Acts 16:30–31, what did Paul say? _____

  _____

  _____

- In John 3:1–18, what did Jesus tell Nicodemus was necessary to be born again (vs. 16)? _____

  _____

Notice what was *not* done in either case. Neither Paul nor Christ said that a special prayer or spiritual task was needed.

- Read Acts 8:36–37. What did the man "do" for salvation? _____
_____
_____

A person isn't saved by praying or following a formula. Rather, we must simply *believe*—or trust—that . . .

- I am a sinner.
- I cannot save myself.
- Christ paid for my sin.
- By trusting Him alone, I will become part of God's family forever.

Be sure the unbeliever understands that the only way of salvation is by trusting Christ—and then get out of the way! Salvation is a transformation that occurs when a person accepts the gift of God. Do not try to reduce it to a simple prayer or formula.

HELP THE YOUNG BELIEVER GROW

A new Christian is like a newborn baby (1 Pet. 2:2). He needs food and nourishment. He needs to grow. It's important that you follow up with a new believer by discipling him. One way to do this is to give him materials—like this book—that will help him begin to study the Bible. You should also encourage him to attend a caring, doctrinally-sound church. Pray with him, study with him, weep with him, and encourage him as he takes these first steps of faith.

Complete This Section Without Looking Back at the Lesson

1. Name three reasons every Christian should witness.
_____
_____
_____
_____
_____
_____

2. List the four major points to emphasize when witnessing and give a Scripture reference for each point.

_____

_____

_____

_____

_____

_____

_____

_____

3. Do we make ourselves Christians by praying a prayer? What is the only thing that the Bible teaches is our responsibility? _____

_____

_____

4. Once a person has trusted in Christ, what are some ways you could help him grow?_____

_____

_____

_____

_____

_____

Verses to Memorize

- Romans 3:23
- Romans 6:23
- Romans 5:8
- Romans 10:9

7

BAPTISM

If you've attended a church long enough, you may have seen someone baptized. But what does this practice mean? How important is it? Why do people decide to be baptized?

In this lesson, you will discover that baptism is a significant step in every believer's life. Let's explore its importance and meaning.

> *Baptism isn't that important, is it?*

BAPTISM IS IMPORTANT

- Read Luke 3:21, 22. According to these verses, before Christ ever began His public ministry, what did He do?

  _____

- In Acts 10:47–48, what did Peter immediately say needed to be done for the new believers? _____

  _____

- By their example and teaching, did Christ and Peter seem to think that baptism was unimportant? ☐ Yes ☐ No

> *Why should we be baptized?*

THE PURPOSE OF BAPTISM

The Bible clearly teaches the importance of baptism, but what is its purpose?

Baptism Does Not Save Us

We are redeemed only by the grace of God, so baptism is not necessary for our salvation, which is a free gift.

- Read Acts 10:44–48 carefully. Did the people believe and receive the Holy Spirit—that is, they were saved—before or after they were baptized? _____

- Read Acts 8:35–38. What response did the eunuch have to Philip's teaching? _____

- Did the eunuch believe before or after his baptism?

_____

Then what is baptism?

Baptism Is a Picture

In Christ's day, people were baptized to publicly demonstrate their repentance or their relationship with a group or teacher. When they were ready to be baptized, someone would usually help immerse them briefly in a body of water.

For Christians, baptism became a way to picture our salvation through God. When a person is baptized, he normally goes through three positions that represent Christ's work. Note the following steps:

- Standing in the water, symbolizing Christ's death
- Placed under the water, symbolizing Christ's burial
- Coming up out of the water, symbolizing Christ's resurrection

Thus, baptism pictures three things that happen to the believer now that he is in Christ.

1. _He is dead with Christ._ How do Galatians 2:20 and Colossians 3:3 explain this statement?

   _____

   _____

   _____

2. _He is buried with Christ._ Read Romans 6:3–4. What does it mean to be buried with Christ?

   _____

   _____

   _____

3. _He is a new creature in Christ, raised with Him to walk in newness of life._ Note Romans 6:4–5 and Colossians 3:1. What must we, as resurrected people, do now?

   _____

   _____

- Second Peter 1:3–5 speaks of a new life. What kind is it?
  _____

- Second Corinthians 5:17 states that if any person is in Christ He is a new _____.
  The old is gone, and we've been made new.

- Read Colossians 3:1–17. What are some things that should be gone from the believer's life (vv. 5–9)?
  _____
  _____
  _____

- What are some new things that a believer will begin to see in their life as they grow in Christ (vv. 10–17)?
  _____
  _____
  _____

Once a new believer understands the importance and meaning of baptism, he should speak with his pastor or church leader about publicly identifying with Christ in this way. It is a once-in-a-lifetime opportunity to confess before others what God has done for us.

Complete This Section Without Looking Back at the Lesson

1. Name two people in the Bible who demonstrated the importance of baptism. _____
  _____

2. How does the salvation story of the Ethiopian treasurer show that a person is not saved by baptism?
  _____
  _____
  _____

3. Name three positions of baptism and what each can picture of Christ's work. _____
  _____
  _____
  _____

4. What three things does baptism picture about the believer's life?_____

_____

_____

_____

_____

Verses to Memorize

- Romans 6:3–4

8

THE BELIEVER AND THE CHURCH

Another vital part of your spiritual growth is your church. Christ never intended His followers to journey through life alone, so He created the church to train, comfort, encourage, and challenge us. The fellowship with believers also gives us opportunities to serve and reflect God's grace to others.

THE IMPORTANCE OF THE CHURCH

Some believers try to serve God outside of the local church. They feel the church has failed, that they can worship God better by gathering in small Bible study groups. They may mean well, but they are not following the teaching of Christ concerning the church.

Christ Instituted the Church as God's Way to Carry out God's Work

Read Matthew 16:18 and Acts 20:28.

- Who builds the church? _____
- To whom does the church belong? _____
- What did He pay for it?_____
- Will the church fail? ☐ Yes   ☐ No

His Church Will Not Fail

Note again Matthew 16:18. Evil will oppose God's church, and some of that evil will masquerade as a church. People claiming to be Christian will nevertheless teach doctrine that contradicts Christ. These so-called believers will lie, hurt, and abuse, destroying the belief of others and perverting the simple truth of the gospel.

But Christ's church will remain. If you find yourself in a church that preaches, teaches, or allows such evil, seek out a fellowship of believers that holds true to the Word, preaches the gospel, and reflects the grace of God. Christ has promised to sustain these believers until His return.

THE NEEDS OF THE CHURCH

Christ sustains His church, and He often uses His followers to do so. The church runs on love, grace, and generosity, and those needs present opportunities for service.

Everything we are and everything we have belongs to God, and He has made us *stewards*—that is, managers—of His property. How we manage His gifts to us will reflect our gratitude to Him. We can worship Him not just in song and praise, but in giving and in service.

Read 1 Peter 4:8–11.

- According to verse 8, what is our first responsibility toward other believers? _____
  _____

- What is one way we can do this (vs. 9)? _____
  _____
  _____

- All this is possible because of a gift given to us by God. According to verse 10, of what are we to be good stewards? _____
  _____

- According to verse 11, what is our goal in all this?
  _____
  _____

God asks us to reach out to others in love, for the praise of His glory. This love can take many forms.

- In 1 Corinthians 12, Christ's church compared to a body—one body, with many members (vs. 12). According to verses 25–26, how should we care for others?
  _____
  _____

Sympathy, time, and care are often more difficult to give than money.

God asks us to give back according to what we have.

- Read 2 Corinthians 8:1–4. In this passage, Paul describes how some believers took up a collection for another group in dire need. How did these believers give (vs. 3)?

  _____

  _____

In the Bible we find the *tithe* as a standard of giving. Normally applied to material possessions, it refers to ten percent of what we earn by our work. In Genesis 14:18–20, we see Abraham offering to God the first tithe recorded in the Bible. Jacob, Abraham's grandson, continued the practice (Gen. 28:20–22); God included it in Israelite law (Lev. 27:30); and Jesus affirmed it (Matt. 23:23), while warning against hypocrisy.

True, sacrificial giving requires more than a little cash or even a hefty check—it means actively identifying needs in the church body and acting on them in love, not for personal credit, but for God's glory. He has given us so much. How can we not share His goodness with others?

THE NECESSITY OF THE CHURCH

Christians Need Fellowship

When you're at school or work, you're probably with many people who do not know the Lord. These are great opportunities to reflect God's light to them, but we all desperately need a time of fellowship with those who can encourage us, challenge us, and teach us about the things of the Lord.

- According to Hebrews 10:24–25, how does God intend for the church—that is, the gathering of believers—to help us? What should we do in church? _____

  _____

  _____

  _____

Christians Need to Be Taught the Word

The early Christians stayed together daily, continuing in the Apostles' doctrine (Acts 2:42). That means they were learning the Word as the Apostles taught them. Acts 6 shows us that the Apostles, who helped lead the first churches, had two major responsibilities—to pray and to teach the Word of God. These duties required time and concentration, and for this reason *deacons*—that is, ministers or servants—were selected.

- According to Acts 6:1–4, were the first deacons chosen to do?_____

_____

Most good churches have a Sunday school or other classroom teaching sessions, as well as services that include preaching. You might also have prayer meetings, small group Bible studies, outreach ministries, and more. No two churches will have the same types of services, organizational structure, or ministries, but whatever your church offers, take the time to meet people, get involved, and show love. Pray for your brothers and sisters in Christ. Let God show you His grace through them, and let Him use you to show grace right back. Be encouraged, be challenged, and be faithful. Love as Christ loves you.

Complete This Section Without Looking Back at the Lesson

1. What institution has Christ built up as His channel for ministry? _____

2. Should we reject the idea of churches since some churches teach falsehood or fail to display Christlike character? ☐ Yes   ☐ No

3. If your church does not teach the truth, what should you do?_____

4. What is a *steward*?_____

_____

5. What does *tithe* mean? _____

_____

6. Name two ways that believers need the church.

_____

_____

_____

7. Write down a few ways that you believe you could start serving in your church. _____

_____

_____

_____

_____

_____

Verses to Memorize

- Hebrews 10:25
- 1 Peter 4:10

EXAMINATION QUESTIONS

Complete the following questions without looking back in your book for answers.

1. In your own words, state whether you are a Christian, along with how you know you are saved. _____

   _____

   _____

   _____

   _____

   _____

2. How many people have sinned? _____

3. What are the wages for sin? _____

4. What must a person do to be saved? _____

   _____

   _____

5. Can an unbeliever naturally do anything right or pleasing to God? ☐ Yes   ☐ No

6. How do our attempts at good deeds appear to God?

   _____

   _____

7. Write out Ephesians 2:8–9 from memory. _____

   _____

   _____

   _____

   _____

   _____

8. What passage in the Bible teaches that you can know you have eternal life? _____

9. What verses teach that you are in God's hands?

   _____

10. Write out Romans 10:9 from memory. _____

    _____

    _____

    _____

11. How much of God's Word is true? _____

12. Name five blessings that come from studying God's Word. _____

_____

_____

_____

_____

13. Why was God's Word written? _____

_____

_____

14. List three ways you should treat the Word of God.

_____

_____

_____

15. Write out 2 Timothy 2:15 from memory. _____

_____

_____

_____

_____

16. What is the key to Bible study presented in this book?

_____

_____

_____

17. Summarize the Story of God's Glory. _____

_____

_____

_____

_____

_____

18. What are the results of seeing God's glory in the Bible?

_____

_____

19. Who can understand God's Word? _____

_____

20. Write out 1 Corinthians 2:14 from memory.

_____

_____

_____

_____

_____

21. What is prayer? _____

_____

22. What one thing hinders prayer? _____

23. To whom, in whose name, and in whose power should you pray? _____

_____

_____

_____

24. Write out 1 Timothy 2:8 from memory.

_____

_____

_____

_____

25. Name four reasons to share your faith.

_____

_____

_____

_____

_____

26. List the four major points to emphasize when witnessing, giving Scripture for each point. _____

_____

_____

_____

_____

_____

27. What passages of Scripture are especially good to use when helping someone find assurance of his salvation?

_____

_____

28. What are two things you can do to help a new believer grow? _____

_____

_____

29. Write out Romans 5:8 from memory. _____

_____

_____

_____

30. Why is a person baptized? _____

_____

31. What are three positions in baptism, and what do they represent? _____

_____

_____

_____

32. What institution has Christ built as a channel for ministry and service? _____

33. Name two reasons why believers need to meet with other believers. _____

_____

_____

_____

34. If your church does not preach the truth, what should you do? _____

_____

_____

35. Who owns the church? _____
    What did He pay for it?_____

_____

Congratulations on completing the *Milk* booklet! We trust God has used the study of His Word to grow and strengthen you in your faith. We pray that you'll continue walking with God, trusting His grace to shape you into His image.

If you have any questions or comments about this study, we'd love to hear from you! You can reach us at info@positiveaction.org, or by calling (800) 688-3008. More Bible study materials, including *Meat*, the next book in this series, are available at positiveaction.org.